PUPPY'S

1ST YEAR

First published by Parragon Books Ltd 2014

Parragon
Chartist House
15-17 Trim Street
Bath BA1 1HA, UK
www.parragon.com

Copyright © Parragon Books Ltd 2014
Produced by Tall Tree Ltd
Illustrations by the Apple Art Agency

ISBN 978-1-4723-3775-7

Printed in China

PUPPY'S
1ST YEAR

SHAWN SHERRY

WOOF

PaRragon

Bath · New York · Singapore · Hong Kong · Cologne · Delhi
Melbourne · Amsterdam · Johannesburg · Shenzhen

PREPARING FOR PUPPY

BEFORE I ARRIVED, MY OWNER BOUGHT ME:

- ☐ A BED OR BLANKET
- ☐ A CHEW TOY
- ☐ A COLLAR
- ☐ A NAME TAG
- ☐ A BALL TO CHASE IN THE PARK
- ☐ A LEAD FOR WALKIES
- ☐ A DOG BOWL
- ☐ SOME YUMMY PUPPY TREATS
- ☐ PUPPY FOOD
- ☐ PUPPY SHAMPOO
- ☐ A BRUSH FOR MY COAT
- ☐ ....
- ☐ ....
- ☐ ....
- ☐ ....

4

stick in a photo
of your puppy
during their
first day at home

my first day at home

MY NAME IS

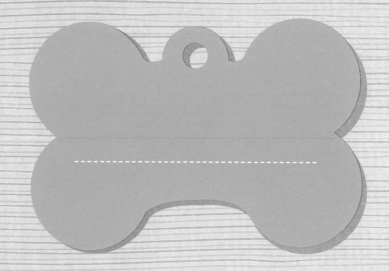

I was called this because...

....

....

....

....

BREED:

COLOUR:

DISTINCTIVE MARKINGS:

SEX:

DATE OF BIRTH:

PLACE OF BIRTH:

THERE WERE: OTHER PUPPIES IN MY LITTER

DETAILS OF MY PARENTS:

please look after me

COMING HOME

ON MY FIRST DAY AT HOME I MET:

I PLAYED WITH: IN THE:

MY FAVOURITE TOY IS THE:

I ATE: FOR MY DINNER

On my first day in my new home I...

_____

_____

_____

_____

_____

_____

_____

_____

_____

_____

_____

_____

stick in a photo
of your puppy
looking cute

SWEET!

10

SITTING PRETTY

stick in a
photo of your
puppy getting
into mischief

GETTING INTO TROUBLE

11

LIST OF FIRSTS

THIS IS HOW I REACTED WHEN...

I FIRST MET ANOTHER DOG:

....

....

I FIRST SAW A CAT:

....

....

I FIRST WENT SWIMMING:

....

....

....

....

....

MY FIRST NIGHT IN MY NEW HOME

stick in a photo
of your puppy in
their new bed

BEFORE I GO TO BED I:

snooze time

MY BED IS IN THE:

....

MY BEDTIME IS AT:

....

I GO TO SLEEP WITH:

....

I WAKE UP AT:

....

NOTES ON HOW I SLEEP:

....

....

....

....

....

Q.WHY DO DOGS DREAM
ABOUT RUNNING
IN CIRCLES?
A.BECAUSE IT'S TOO
HARD TO RUN
IN SQUARES.

15

MY NEW FAMILY

THE PEOPLE WHO LIVE IN MY NEW HOME WITH ME ARE:
....
....

THEY ALSO OWN THESE PETS:
....
....

I CUDDLE: THE MOST, BECAUSE:
....

I PLAY WITH: THE MOST, BECAUSE:
....
....

THE PERSON WHO CLEANS UP AFTER ME THE MOST IS:
....
....

WOOF

stick in a photo
of your puppy
with their
new family

ME AND MY NEW FAMILY

stick in a photo
of your puppy
during their
first week
at home

TIME TO
EXPLORE!

my first week at home

18

stick in a photo
of your puppy
during their
second week
at home

my second week at home

MY FIRST WALK

🐾 FOR MY FIRST WALK WE WENT TO:

....

....

🐾 THE WEATHER WAS:

....

🐾 ON THE WAY, WE SAW THESE OTHER BREEDS OF DOG:

....

....

....

....

🐾 WHO TAKES ME FOR A WALK:

🐾 DURING A WALK I LIKE TO:

🐾 MY OWNER TAKES THESE THINGS WHEN WE GO FOR A WALK:

A GOOD EDUCATION

RECORD THE INSTRUCTIONS YOU GIVE YOUR PUPPY AND GRADE HOW WELL THEY DO, FROM A TO E.

MY OWNER SAYS: _____ WHEN THEY WANT ME TO SIT.

A B C D E

THEY SAY: _____ WHEN THEY WANT ME TO STAY STILL.

A B C D E

THEY SAY: _____ WHEN THEY WANT ME TO LIE DOWN.

A B C D E

THEY SAY: _____ WHEN I'VE PICKED UP SOMETHING EEUCH AND THEY WANT ME TO DROP IT.

A B C D E

GOOD DOG!

MY OWNER SAYS: _____ WHEN THEY WANT ME TO FETCH SOMETHING.

A   B   C   D   E

THEY SAY: _____ WHEN THEY WANT ME TO GO TO MY BED.

A   B   C   D   E

THEY SAY: _____ WHEN THEY WANT ME TO WALK NICELY BY THEM.

A   B   C   D   E

THEY SAY: _____ WHEN THEY WANT ME TO RUN OVER TO THEM.

A   B   C   D   E

WHEN I'M LEARNING THESE TASKS MY OWNER REWARDS ME WITH:

How did I do?

Mostly As: perfect
Mostly Bs: top dog
Mostly Cs: doing OK
Mostly Ds: could do better
Mostly Es: needs more work

23

I LIKE TO CHEW...

GOOD!

MUNCH AND CRUNCH!

1 ....

2 ....

3 ....

4 ....

5 ....

I'M NOT SUPPOSED TO CHEW...

BAD!

1 _____

2 _____

3 _____

4 _____

5 _____

WRECK AND RUIN!

MY FAVOURITE FOODS ARE...

YUM!

1 _____

2 _____

3 _____

4 _____

5 _____

26

BUT I DON'T LIKE...

1 ....

2 ....

3 ....

4 ....

5 ....

YUK!

enjoying my food

stick in a
photo of your
puppy enjoying
their food

stick in a
photo of your
puppy playing
with their
favourite toy

playing with my favourite toy

MY FAVOURITE TOYS ARE...

★★★★★ --

★★★★★ --

★★★★★ --

★★★★★ --

★★★★★ --

Make a list of your puppy's favourite toys and score how much they are loved using the star rating.

WOOF

Q. WHAT DO YOU CALL YOUNG DOGS
WHO LIKE TO PLAY IN THE SNOW?
A. SLUSH PUPPIES.

PLAYTIME!

Stick in some photos to create
a playful canine collage.

SNIFFING

Q. WHY IS A TREE
LIKE A BIG DOG?
A. THEY BOTH HAVE A
LOT OF BARK.

chasing

ON THE PROWL

I DON'T LIKE THESE...

- ☐ LOUD NOISES
- ☐ SMALL CHILDREN
- ☐ THE DARK
- ☐ BEING LEFT ALONE
- ☐ THE RAIN
- ☐ CARS
- ☐ OTHER DOGS
- ☐ WATER
- ☐ BATH TIME

- ☐ BALLOONS
- ☐ FIREWORKS
- ☐ MOTORBIKES

OTHER THINGS I DON'T LIKE ARE:

....

....

....

....

....

When I get frightened, I...

RUN AND HIDE!

GOOD GROOMING

🐾 I HAVE A BATH EVERY:
....

🐾 I ENJOY/DISLIKE MY BATH TIME BECAUSE:
....
....
....

🐾 MY COAT IS COMBED EVERY:
....

🐾 MY COAT NEEDS THESE SPECIAL TREATMENTS:
....
....
....
....

🐾 I HAVE THIS TYPE OF COAT:

....

....

🐾 MY OWNER HAS THESE GROOMING TOOLS:

....

....

....

....

....

....

PAMPERED PET

stick in a photo
of your puppy
being groomed

NICE GROOMING

stick in a photo
of your puppy
going for a walk

GOING FOR A WALK

WALKIES!

I GO FOR A WALK: TIMES A DAY
....

I NEED: MINUTES' WALKING A DAY
....

I LIKE TO GO EXPLORING TO:
....
....
....

MY FAVOURITE WALK IS:
....
....

MY FAVOURITE THING TO DO WHEN OUT ON A WALK IS:
....
....
....

I LIKE TO SNIFF:
....
....
....

WE ALWAYS MEET:
....
....
....

Time to go

PUPPY FRIENDS

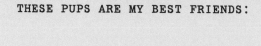

THESE PUPS ARE MY BEST FRIENDS:

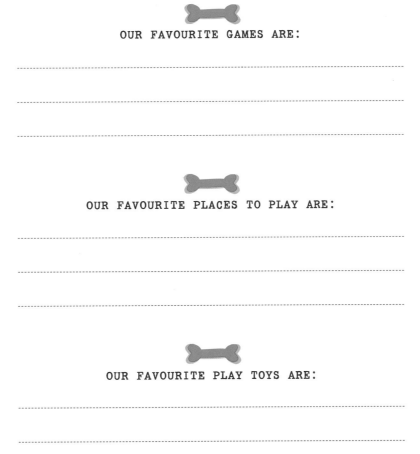

OUR FAVOURITE GAMES ARE:

....
....
....

OUR FAVOURITE PLACES TO PLAY ARE:

....
....
....

OUR FAVOURITE PLAY TOYS ARE:

....
....
....

TIME FOR A NAP

I LIKE TO TAKE A NAP AT AROUND _____ EVERY DAY.

I SLEEP ON MY FRONT ⬭ BACK ⬭ SIDE ⬭

MY FAVOURITE PLACES TO NAP ARE:

....

....

....

....

photos of
me napping

stick in a photo
of your puppy
on the prowl

BIG, BRAVE
HUNTER

ON THE PROWL

stick in a photo
of your puppy
chewing on their
favourite toy

FAVOURITE TOY

MY FIRST CHRISTMAS

ON CHRISTMAS MORNING WE:

....

....

....

....

I WAS GIVEN THESE PRESENTS:

....

....

....

....

stick in a photo
of your puppy at
Christmas time

Happy Christmas!

HEALTH CARE

MY VET'S NAME IS:
....

MY VET'S ADDRESS IS:
....

....

....

....

MY VET'S PHONE NUMBER IS:
....

I TAKE THESE TO KEEP ME HEALTHY...

I TAKE .... EVERY .... DAYS
....

I TAKE .... EVERY .... DAYS
....

I TAKE .... EVERY .... DAYS

SO THAT I DON'T HAVE FLEAS
....

MAKE IT BETTER

I AM VACCINATED AGAINST:

(Y) HAVE I BEEN MICROCHIPPED? (N)

MY MICROCHIP NUMBER IS:

INSURANCE DETAILS:

MY TRAVELS

I HAVE BEEN ON TRIPS TO:

CITY BREAKS

BY THE SEA

COUNTRY RETREAT

HOLIDAY HOME

🐾 MY FAVOURITE PLACE WAS _____ BECAUSE:

....

....

....

....

🐾 I HAVE STAYED WITH THESE PEOPLE:

....

....

....

....

🐾 WHEN MY OWNER GOES AWAY, I STAY AT:

....

....

....

....

....

53

stick in a photo
of your puppy on
their travels

ON HOLIDAY

stick in a photo
of your puppy on
the beach

PUPPY IQ TEST

HERE ARE SOME SIMPLE TESTS TO SEE HOW SMART I AM.

WHEN I HEAR A NEW SOUND I:

A. ◯ TRY TO FIND THE SOUND

B. ◯ RAISE MY HEAD AND LOOK

C. ◯ DON'T REACT

DOES YOUR DOG JUMP WHEN YOU GIVE A COMMAND, OR JUST 'PAWS' FOR A TREAT?

WHEN I'M IN A NEW PLACE I:

A. ◯ EXPLORE EVERY SQUARE INCH

B. ◯ SNIFF CAUTIOUSLY

C. ◯ FALL ASLEEP

WHEN I SEE MY REFLECTION I:

A. ◯ GET EXCITED

B. ◯ WAG MY TAIL THEN LOSE INTEREST

C. ◯ WALK AWAY

WHEN I'M STROKED I:

A. ◯ LIFT MY HEAD TO GET A BETTER STROKE

B. ◯ SHAKE MY HEAD

C. ◯ PULL AWAY

WHEN THERE ARE OBSTACLES ON THE PATH, SUCH AS STICKS, I:

A. ◯ STEP OVER THEM CAREFULLY

B. ◯ STEP OVER THEM, BUT HIT A FEW

C. ◯ REFUSE TO WALK NEAR THE OBSTACLES

MOSTLY As: GENIUS

MOSTLY Bs: OK

MOSTLY Cs: NEEDS WORK

MY OWNER LOVES ME BECAUSE...

TICK THE CHARACTERISTICS THAT BEST SUIT YOUR PUP

- ♡ I'M CUTE

- ♡ I'M ALWAYS READY TO PLAY

- ♡ I LIKE CUDDLES

SWEET

- ♡ I LIKE WALKS

- ♡ I ENJOY MEETING PEOPLE

- ♡ I'M FRIENDLY

I AM VERY FUNNY

I MAKE MY OWNER HAPPY

I'M OBEDIENT

I'M PLAYFUL

I'M KOOKY

I'M EAGER TO PLEASE

I'M SHY

I'M BOISTEROUS

I LOVE MY OWNER TOO

MY FIRST BIRTHDAY

FOR MY BIRTHDAY I WAS GIVEN:

I CELEBRATED MY BIRTHDAY BY:

FOR MY BIRTHDAY DINNER, I HAD:

----

stick in a photo
of your puppy
celebrating
their birthday

HAPPY BIRTHDAY TO ME!

QUICK NOTE:

stick in a photo
of your puppy
when they first
arrived home

look how I've grown

ONE YEAR OLD

SMILE, PLEASE!

stick in a photo
of your puppy
aged one year

WOOF

USEFUL CONTACTS

TRAINING:
....
....
....
....

WELFARE:
....
....
....
....

VETS:
....
....
....
....